£1-50

oasis don't believe the truth

TURN UP THE SUN 2
MUCKY FINGERS 7
LYLA 12
LOVE LIKE A BOMB 18
THE IMPORTANCE OF BEING IDLE 22
THE MEANING OF SOUL 26
GUESS GOD THINKS I'M ABEL 30
PART OF THE QUEUE 35
KEEP THE DREAM ALIVE 40
A BELL WILL RING 47
LET THERE BE LOVE 52

Exclusive distributors:
Music Sales Limited
8/9 Frith Street, London W1D 3JB, England.
Music Sales Pty Limited
120 Rothschild Avenue, Rosebery, NSW 2018, Australia.

Order No. AM92240
ISBN 0-7119-4365-6
This book © Copyright 2005 by Wise Publications,
a division of Music Sales Limited.

Music arrangements by Derek Jones.
Music processed by Paul Ewers Music Design.

Printed in the United Kingdom by
Caligraving Limited, Thetford, Norfolk.

www.musicsales.com

Your Guarantee of Quality:

As publishers, we strive to produce every book
to the highest commercial standards.

The music has been freshly engraved to make
playing from it a real pleasure. Particular care has been given
to specifying acid-free, neutral-sized paper made from pulps
which have not been elemental chlorine bleached.

This pulp is from farmed sustainable forests and
was produced with special regard for the environment.

Throughout, the printing and binding have been
planned to ensure a sturdy, attractive publication
which should give years of enjoyment.

If your copy fails to meet our high standards,
please inform us and we will gladly replace it.

Wise Publications
part of The Music Sales Group

London / New York / Paris / Sydney / Copenhagen / Berlin / Madrid / Tokyo

3 4130 00109727 0

TURN UP THE SUN

Words & Music by Andy Bell

You should-n't take___ it as a re-flec-tion on you.___

Come on,___ turn up the sun.___ Turn it up for ev - 'ry- one.___

Love one a - no - ther. Love one a - no - ther.

2. The boys in the bub - ble, they wan-na be free.___

Love one a - no - ther.

Love one a - no - ther.

MUCKY FINGERS

Words & Music by Noel Gallagher

1. I know you think you de - serve_ an ex - pla -
2. And when you look in that mir - ror and you're

It's all___ mine!!___

It's all___ mine!!

LYLA

Words & Music by Noel Gallagher

Original key: B Major
Guitar capo third fret

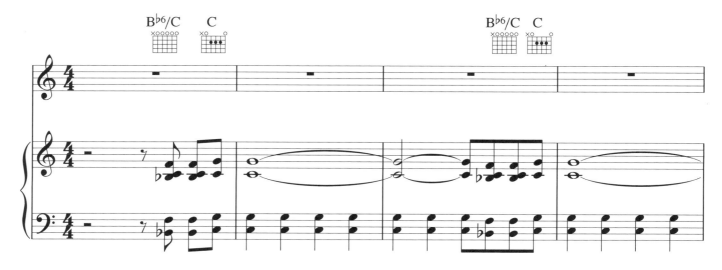

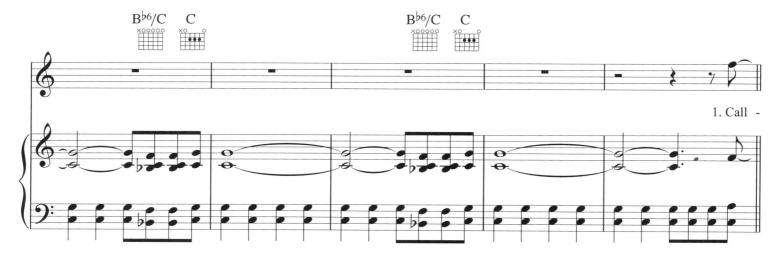

1. Call -

-in' all the stars to fall and catch the sil-ver sun-

LOVE LIKE A BOMB

Words & Music by Liam Gallagher & Gem Archer

1. see - ing_____ a whole noth - er world_ in my mind.
(2.) reach - in'_____ the world that I want_ deep in - side.
(3.) see - ing,_____ a whole noth - er world_ in my mind.

Girl, I'm feel - ing_____ an' breath-ing in love__ all the
Girl, I mean it,_____ an' you hold the key__ to the
Girl, I'm feel - ing_____ that we've been in love__ all the

time.   You turn me on,_____
shrine.   'Cos you turn me on,_____   yer love's like a bomb,__
time.   'Cos you turn me on,_____

__ yer blow- in' my mind.   You turn me on,__

__ yer love's like a bomb,__   yer blow- in' my   mind.

To Coda ⊕

THE IMPORTANCE OF BEING IDLE

Words & Music by Noel Gallagher

THE MEANING OF SOUL

Words & Music by Liam Gallagher

If it's al - - - right then I'll be your light.

Guitar ad lib.

Harmonica ad lib.

GUESS GOD THINKS I'M ABEL

Words & Music by Liam Gallagher

1. I could be____ your lov-

34

PART OF THE QUEUE

Words & Music by Noel Gallagher

1. Sud - den - ly I found that I'd
2. names on the fa - ces in pla -
3° *Instrumental till ***

lost my way in this ci - ty. The
- ces, they mean no - thing to me. It's

streets and the thou - sands of col - ours all bleed in - to____
all they can do____ to be part of all the queue in this____

one.____ I fall____ down,
town.____ I fall____ down,

Hea - ven won't help me. I call_____ out,
Hea - ven won't help me. I call_____ out,

no - one would hear.____ All of a sud - den I'd lost my way out of the
no - one will hear.____ There'll be no to - mor - row they say, well I say more's the

39

KEEP THE DREAM ALIVE

Words & Music by Andy Bell

41

45

Na   na   na_____   na   na_____   na   na._____

Repeat to fade

46

A BELL WILL RING

Words & Music by Gem Archer

1. A

47

Come a - live,___ come on in,___ here's some - thing that___ you know.___
tell you what you wan - na hear, I've been___ there once___ be - fore.___

The world's as wide___ as your life is thin___ so en -
You___ pulled me through___ my emp - ty nights, sleep -

- ter - tain___ your goals.___
- less on___ your floor.___

The sun___ will shine___ on you___

And all____ will be____ brand new.____

LET THERE BE LOVE

Words & Music by Noel Gallagher

waiting for you. May all your dreaming fill the empty sky.

But if it makes you happy,

keep on clapping. Just remember I'll be by your

side. And if you don't let go it's gonna pass you by.

54

3. Who kicked a